Back to Basics

ENGLISH

for 10–11 year olds

BOOK TWO

Sheila Lane and Marion Kemp

Alphabetical order

Write the complete alphabet.

| A | | | | | | | | | | | | | | | | | | | | | | | | | |

Write the missing letters in each series.

1 C D ☐ F G ☐ I J ☐ L M ☐ ☐ O P   **4** ☐ ☐ C ☐ ☐ ☐ G ☐ ☐ J ☐ ☐ ☐

2 ☐ ☐ Q R ☐ T U ☐ W X ☐ ☐   **5** A ☐ ☐ ☐ E ☐ G ☐ ☐ ☐ K ☐ M

3 Z ☐ X ☐ V ☐ T ☐ R ☐ P

Write these authors' names in **alphabetical order**.

Dahl ....

Grimm ....

Blume ....

Shakespeare ....

Fine ....

Anderson ....

Write these musicians' names in **alphabetical order**.

Beethoven ....

Byrd ....

Bach ....

Brahms ....

Borodin ....

Bizet ....

When the words in a set begin with the **same** letter, look at the **second** letter of each word. If they begin with the **same two letters**, look at the **third** and so on.

Write these sets of words in **alphabetical order**.

spear ....

spend ....

spell ....

special ....

speed ....

contract ....

contour ....

continue ....

contempt ....

contact ....

birthday ....

birthplace ....

baby ....

between ....

baptize ....

Challenge   Write the nouns, all beginning with the same three letters, under each picture.

Write the nouns in alphabetical order.

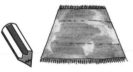

....

....

....

....

....

....

An **index** is an **alphabetical list** which you can use when looking up **information**.

Draw a line under the important **key word** in each phrase.
Write the page number where you would find the information in the box.

1 leopard-<u>fish</u> coloration

2 habits of Goliath beetles

3 edible molluscs

4 life-history of the natterjack toad

5 St. Bernard dogs at work

6 Australian coral reefs

7 habitat of honey birds

8 uses of angora rabbit fur

INDEX	page
Beetles	36
Birds	23
Corals	42
Dogs	16
Fish	30
Molluscs	39
Rabbits	19
Toads	25

Write **true** or **false** for each definition:

1 ancient   : belonging to the future

2 century   : a hundred years

3 crusade   : a holy war

4 decade   : a period of fifty years

5 medieval   : modern times

6 monarch   : a king, queen or emperor

7 monastery : a building where politicians live

8 reign   : part of a horse's harness

Check your answers by using your dictionary. Put a tick or a cross in the boxes.

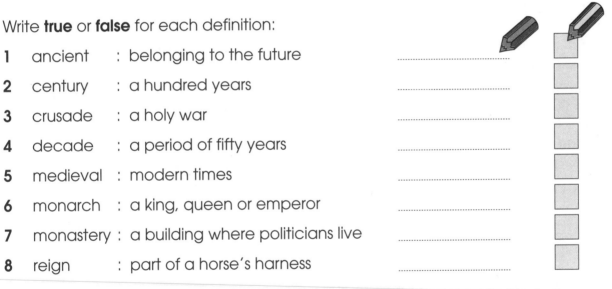

Find a **compound** word in your dictionary having the **prefix** 'land' for these definitions:

.... a view of the countryside

.... someone who owns a large amount of land

.... a keeper of an inn or lodging place which has tenants

.... a fall of earth or rocks from a cliff or mountain

.... an object on a landscape which is easily seen

Comprehension

Read about **Journey to the Centre of the Earth**, by Jules Verne.

In this story, Professor Lidenbrock finds an old book about Iceland. Inside is a document covered with strange signs. Axel, the Professor's nephew, discovers that the signs are an ancient alphabet. He deciphers the message which says:

> GO DOWN INSIDE THE SNEFFELS VOLCANO ON THE LAST DAY
> IN JUNE AND YOU WILL JOURNEY TO THE CENTRE OF THE EARTH.
> I HAVE DONE THIS
>
> ARNE SOKNUSSEMM

The Professor and Axel set off for Iceland and engage a local guide, named Hans. The three of them begin to scale the slopes of the Sneffels volcano, but it soon becomes bitterly cold. Axel, unlike his uncle, is a cautious fellow.

'What will become of us if this volcano wakes up when we are inside?' he asks.

The Professor, who is a little mad, laughs.

'Sneffels has been silent for 600 years,' he says, 'but of course, it may speak again.'

At that moment, Hans points down the mountain side.

'MISTOUR! MISTOUR!' he cries.

They look down and see a huge column of stones, sand and dust twisting and swirling towards them.

About the story

Read the question. Put a tick under the correct answer.

1 In the story the Professor finds an old book about:

Greenland	Finland	Iceland	Ireland
☐	☐	☐	☐

2 Axel discovers that the book contains:

a treasure map	an ancient alphabet	a star chart
☐	☐	☐

3 The message tells them to go down:

a quarry	a mine	a volcano
☐	☐	☐

4 To help them on their journey, the Professor engages:

bag carriers	a cook	an Icelandic guide	sledge drivers
☐	☐	☐	☐

What happens in the story

Put these events in order by numbering each line.

.... They set off up the slopes of the volcano.

.... They decide to travel to Iceland.

.... They see a column of stones, sand and dust coming towards them.

......1...... The Professor finds an old book.

.... The Professor engages a local guide.

.... Axel deciphers an ancient alphabet.

About the characters in the story

1   What kind of person was Professor Lidenbrock? ....

....

2   In what way was Axel 'unlike his uncle'? ....

....

How the story is written

1   Write a word or phrase from the story for:

old .... important paper .... employ ....

wary .... eccentric .... without a sound ....

2   The Professor says, 'Sneffels has been silent for 600 years, but of course, it may speak again.' Explain what he means.

....

....

3   Describe the Mistour.

....

....

Handwriting

Using your best joined up handwriting, copy this definition of a volcano.

A volcano is a mountain with an opening through which molten lava, gas and ash flow out when it erupts.

....

....

Grammar

A **verb** can be in the **past**, or the **present**, or the **future**.
This is called the **tense** of the verb.

past	present	future
Yesterday	Today **is**	Tomorrow **will be**
was Friday.	Saturday.	Sunday.

Write **past tense**, **present tense** or **future tense** at the end of each sentence.

1   Tomorrow I will tidy my bedroom.   ....

2   Yesterday I played chess with my brother.   ....

3   Today is my sister's fifth birthday.   ....

4   I went to see my grandmother last week.   ....

5   I am in the school play.   ....

6   Next year I will go to my new school.   ....

Complete these sentences with the **correct tense** of the verb in brackets.

1   My cousin _____ at his new school yesterday.   (start)

2   I _____ _____ with you tomorrow.   (come)

3   It _____ all day last Saturday.   (rain)

4   The fun-fair _____ _____ today.   (open)

5   My grandfather _____ _____ next week.   (arrive)

6   Last year I _____ two lengths.   (swim)

Write each word or phrase in the correct part of the **Time Gauge**.

now

last week

tomorrow

am wearing

the year 1066

see

was

wore

PRESENT TENSE

PAST TENSE

FUTURE TENSE

jumped

sang

is

A.D. 2000

will wear

will be

TIME GAUGE

An **adverb** tells **more** about a **verb**.
It tells us <u>where</u>, <u>when</u> and <u>how</u> the action of the verb takes place.

e.g. She spoke <u>quietly</u>.

Draw a line under the **verb** in each sentence.

Write the **adverb** here.

1   The tortoise moved slowly towards the lettuce.

2   He chewed noisily on the leaves.

3   Soon he wandered away to the shade.

4   Next door's tortoise often visits our garden.

5   He clumsily climbs the low rockery.

6   He sometimes stays all day.

Complete these sentences using words
from the box as **adverbs**.

sideways	
beautifully	
majestically	
always	
angrily	
easily	

1   The bull roared .... at the visitors.

2   The wall collapsed .... onto the pavement.

3   Jenny is .... late for school.

4   I .... answered the teacher's question.

5   The king strode .... onto the platform.

6   The artist painted the picture ....

Write sentences, each containing one of these **adverbs**:

   immediately   desperately   bravely   politely   unhappily   cunningly

1 ....

2 ....

3 ....

4 ....

5 ....

6 ....

Spelling

Make words using be– and re–.

be
- fore ....
- hind ....
- side ....
- siege ....
- low ....

re
- appear ....
- cycle ....
- new ....
- pay ....
- start ....

Use colours to identify word parts made by:

-graph   means 'of writing'

-ology   means 'scientific study of a branch of knowledge'

-scope   means 'instrument for observing or detecting'

biography 1   geology 4   6 autobiography ✓   9 zoology
microscope 2   archaeology 5   7 biology ✓   10 telescope
    paragraph 3   8 sociology

Write the words from the box which have the following meanings:

1 .... an instrument for magnifying tiny things

2 .... the scientific study of rocks

3 .... the written story of someone's life

4 .... the scientific study of animals

5 .... an instrument for seeing distant objects more clearly

6 .... the scientific study of living things

7 .... the digging up and scientific study of ancient remains

8 .... the story of someone's life, written by that person

9 .... a division in a piece of writing

10 .... the study of society

Challenge   Read these words ending with ough.
Draw a ring round the **two** words which **rhyme**.

bough   rough   cough   tough   dough

Read about **The Laboratory**.

In our school laboratory you will see all kinds of equipment. There are thermometers for measuring temperature, a microscope for magnifying tiny things and a box of magnets. In the apparatus cupboard there are test tubes, beakers and flasks for holding liquids. Cylinders are used for measuring the volume of liquids. There are funnels, which are useful for pouring liquids into narrow openings and tripods which are stands or supports with three legs.

Look carefully at the underlined words and then cover over the paragraph.

| **LOOK** | **SAY** | **COVER** | **WRITE** | **CHECK** |
| at each word | each word | each word | from memory | your spelling |

beaker

cylinder

flask

funnel

magnet

microscope

test tube

tripod

Write **meter** (a suffix for a measuring instrument) on each of the following:

alti ....

baro ....

pedo ....

tacho ....

thermo ....

Look up each word in your dictionary. Write the instrument's **use** here.

The thesaurus

A **thesaurus** collects together words which have a **similar meaning** to each other, called **synonyms**.

Laugh, chuckle and smile are **synonyms**.

Write **synonyms** for these **key words**:

key word:	road (noun)		key word:	boat (noun)
synonyms	1 _____		**synonyms**	1 _____
	2 _____			2 _____
	3 _____			3 _____

key word:	seat (noun)		key word:	friend (noun)
synonyms	1 _____		**synonyms**	1 _____
	2 _____			2 _____
	3 _____			3 _____

key word:	story (noun)		key word:	crowd (noun)
synonyms	1 _____		**synonyms**	1 _____
	2 _____			2 _____
	3 _____			3 _____

Draw rings round the two **adjectives** which are synonyms of the word in capital letters.

1	ENORMOUS	immense	slight	massive	elephant
2	DANGEROUS	flag	perilous	red	menacing
3	EXCITING	film	dramatic	play	sensational
4	EMPTY	void	vacant	seat	bucket
5	FAMOUS	person	celebrated	notable	cheerful
6	INDUSTRIOUS	diligent	inactive	busy	sluggish

Draw rings round the two **verbs** which are synonyms of the word in capital letters.

1	START	whistle	commence	begin	continue
2	BURN	char	glow	cook	scorch
3	CHASE	gather	pursue	follow	collect
4	HATE	detest	forbid	dislike	argue
5	CLEAN	rinse	launder	iron	purify
6	OFFEND	displease	defend	involve	insult

A **thesaurus** can help you to choose the best word **for your purpose**.
e.g. sad, cold, lifeless
A dead bird can look sad and cold, but **lifeless** is the best word to describe something **not living**.

Write the best word from the brackets to describe:

1   a <u>boring</u> film   (stodgy, dull, thick)   ....
2   a <u>clever</u> child   (apt, handy, talented)   ....
3   <u>dark</u> dungeons   (tanned, murky, brunette)   ....
4   the <u>right</u> answer   (correct, just, law-abiding)   ....
5   an <u>easy</u> puzzle   (simple, painful, soft)   ....
6   a <u>hard</u> question   (solid, strong, difficult)   ....
7   <u>warm</u> weather   (mild, luke-warm, tepid)   ....
8   an <u>ugly</u> building   (war-like, unsightly, sore)   ....
9   <u>quiet</u> surroundings   (soft, woolly, tranquil)   ....
10 <u>poor</u> refugees   (cheap, faulty, destitute)   ....

Complete these **synonyms** with the correct spelling:

1   giving a strong light

| b | r | | | | t |

| r | | | | a | n | t |

2   a close friend

| c | o | m | | | | i | o | n |

| c | | | | a | d | e |

3   people gathered together

| a | u | d | | | | | |

| c | o | n | g | | | | t | i | o | n |

4   to look carefully into something

| e | x | a | | | | |

| i | n | s | | | | |

5   to see something happen

| o | b | | | | | e |

| w | | | n | e | s | s |

6   worth a lot of money

| p | r | e | | | o | u | s |

| v | | | | a | b | l | e |

7   to find something out

| d | i | s | | | | | r |

| d | | | e | c | t |

8   entirely different

| o | p | p | | | | | |

| c | o | n | | | | | | t | o | r | y |

Making notes

Read each sentence.
Cross out the words **not**
important to the meaning.

Write the **key words**
in each sentence.

1   Henry VIII was born in the year 1491.

2   Henry reigned between the years 1509 and 1547.

3   Over the years Cardinal Wolsey became Lord Chancellor.

4   Wolsey used his power to make himself very rich.

5   Hampton Court Palace was built by the wealthy Wolsey.

....
....
....
....
....
....
....
....
....

Write **key words** for each sentence
as **notes**.

1   Henry's second wife, Anne Boleyn, was the mother of Elizabeth.

2   Elizabeth the First became Queen of England in the year 1558.

3   She reigned for 45 years and during that time she had many favourites.

4   One of Elizabeth's favourites was Sir Walter Raleigh, who was a poet, a soldier and an explorer.

5   Elizabeth gave Thomas Tallis, the musician, the work of composing and printing music for her court.

6   During Elizabethan times, William Shakespeare, a young writer, wrote over thirty-seven plays and many poems.

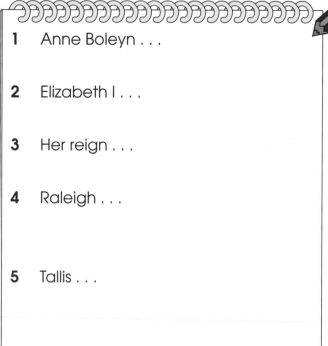

1   Anne Boleyn . . .

2   Elizabeth I . . .

3   Her reign . . .

4   Raleigh . . .

5   Tallis . . .

6   Shakespeare . . .

Read these sentences about
Sir Francis Drake:

Write the **key words** in each
sentence as **notes**.

1   Sir Francis Drake was a famous sailor
    in the reign of Elizabeth I.

....

....

2   The Queen gave Drake permission to
    attack ships from other countries, and
    take their cargoes.

....

....

3   Drake sailed into Spanish ports in
    America and stole their gold for the
    Queen.

....

....

4   The Spaniards nick-named Drake
    El Draco, which means The Dragon.

....

....

Read these paragraphs about
The Armada:

Write **notes** as answers to
these questions:

Information	Questions	Useful notes
In the year 1588 a Spanish fleet, under the command of Admiral Medina Sidonia, set sail for England. The Armada sailed up the English Channel to invade England.	1 Who was the Spanish Admiral? 2 When did he set sail? 3 Which way did the Armada come? 4 Why did he come?	
After sailing into a violent storm, the Armada sheltered in Calais harbour. While they waited, Drake attacked them with his fire ships.	5 Where did the Armada take shelter? 6 Why did they do this? 7 What did Drake do?	
As soon as the Spaniards were driven out to the open sea, a violent storm destroyed many of their ships. Of the 130 ships which had set out from Spain, only 60 returned.	8 What happened when the Spaniards were driven out to the open sea? 9 How many ships had set out from Spain? 10 How many returned?	

Punctuation

' This is an **apostrophe**.
One use of an apostrophe is to show where letters have been missed out in the **shortened forms** of words.

> e.g. is<u>n'</u>t for is <u>not</u> is called a **contraction**.

Write the contraction for:

1	I will _I'll_	4	you are _____	7	did not _____
2	you have _____	5	she is _____	8	will not _____
3	we are _____	6	they are _____	9	could not _____

Apostrophes **'** are also used with the letter **s** to show ownership.
When the noun is singular, add **s after the apostrophe**.

> e.g. 'the robin**'s** nest' for 'the nest belonging to the robin'

Write each phrase with an apostrophe to show ownership:

1 the tail of the dog _____

2 the coat of Harry _____

3 the pouch of the kangaroo _____

4 the summit of Mount Everest _____

5 the canoe of the Inuit _____

The **apostrophe** always follows the owner word.
When the noun is plural, add the **apostrophe after the s**.

> e.g. the girl**s'** hats
> The **s** shows that there is more than one girl owning the hats.

Underline the phrase which uses the apostrophe correctly for each picture.

the hen's eggs
the hens' eggs

the girl's kites
the girls' kites

the bee's wings
the bees' wings

an aeroplanes' wings
an aeroplane's wings

the monkeys' tail
the monkey's tail

the clowns' noses
the clown's noses

Punctuation revision

Space the words. Write the sentences with correct capital letters and punctuation marks.

1 thesunsetovertheseahungryseagullsswoopeddownoverthewaves

....

....

2 afullmooncastabeamoflightthroughthetreestherewasthemissingdoghewashiding underthethickleafybushes

....

....

....

Write the correct punctuation marks in each ring.

| full stop | comma | question mark | inverted commas | apostrophe | exclamation mark |

Add the correct punctuation marks to these sentences:

1 Stand cried the highwayman or I shoot

2 Hand over your jewels he commanded

3 Must you take everything we have quavered the frightened travellers

4 I take all replied Turpin Now drive on

Underline the owner word. Write each owner word with an apostrophe.

1 a birds nest ....

2 two cats eyes ....

3 many ships masts ....

4 several girls rings ....

5 a donkeys tail ....

6 an authors book ....

Write these words as abbreviations.

miles per hour ....

please turn over ....

Rest In Peace ....

Football Association ....

Elizabeth Regina ....

New York ....

Vocabulary

A **homophone** is a word having the **same sound** as another word, but a **different meaning**.

e.g. pear and pair

Say each word aloud. Write another word which **sounds** exactly the same.

scent _____	flour _____	whole _____	sum _____
bawl _____	knew _____	write _____	grate _____
stair _____	route _____	prophet _____	soar _____
peace _____	cereal _____	stile _____	wring _____

Write the meaning of each of these homophones. Use your dictionary to help you.

rain _____	so _____
reign _____	sew _____
rein _____	sow _____

you _____	vain _____
yew _____	vane _____
ewe _____	vein _____

Complete each sentence with **one** of the words from the brackets.

1 [sight / site] The building _____ was a pile of rubble.

2 [four / for] There are _____ quarters in one whole.

3 [main / mane] The electrician switched off the _____ current.

4 [stationary / stationery] The motorist collided with a _____ car.

Challenge Some words can be used as nouns, verbs or adjectives.
e.g. a brave (noun) is a Native American warrior
      to brave something (verb) means to defy something
      brave (adjective) means able to face danger

Write a phrase giving the meaning of:

a light (noun) _____

to light (verb) _____

light (adjective) _____

An **analogy** is a comparison which shows a relationship between **two** things.

e.g. birds fly in the air   fish swim in the sea

so . . . birds are to air **as** fish are to sea

Draw a ring round the word in the brackets which makes the best **analogy** in each of the following:

1   foot is to ankle as hand is to (toe, wrist, leg)

2   horse is to hoof as cat is to (whiskers, tail, paw)

3   ear is to hearing as eye is to (sight, eyelid, taste)

4   nose is to smell as hand is to (finger, nail, touch)

5   butcher is to meat as florist is to (medicine, flowers, fruit)

6   newsagent is to newspapers as fishmonger is to (comics, fish, sweets)

7   cowman is to cattle as shepherd is to (sheep, hens, goats)

8   teacher is to school as doctor is to (hospital, library, kiosk)

9   glove is to hand as slipper is to (mitten, foot, leg)

10   large is to small as wide is to (river, narrow, tall)

Write a missing **analogy** in each of the following:

1   girl is to daughter as _____ is to son

2   herd is to cows as _____ is to bees

3   lion is to lioness as _____ is to mare

4   king is to queen as _____ is to princess

5   start is to begin as _____ is to end

6   friend is to ally as _____ is to foe

7   pleasant is to agreeable as _____ is to disagreeable

8   solid is to firm as _____ is to fluid

9   antonym is to synonym as _____ is to wet

10   famine is to food as _____ is to water

Challenge	If . . . ATTACK means

a small nail . . .

what could YELLOW mean?

_____

Standard English

Draw a ring round (**no**) in these negatives:

not   none   nothing   no-one   nobody   nowhere

Two negatives should **never** be used together in one sentence.

I never saw nothing.

That means you did see something!

Write the correct word from the brackets to complete each sentence.

1 [nothing / anything] She did not tell me _____ about it.

2 [no / any] Haven't you got _____ money to spend?

3 [never / ever] Won't you _____ shut that door?

4 [anywhere / nowhere] I couldn't find my coat _____ .

5 [nobody / anybody] We did not see _____ when we went out early.

6 [ever / never] Nothing _____ happens in my family.

The **prefix 'non'**, meaning <u>not</u>, can give an opposite meaning.

Write the meanings of these words. Use your dictionary to help you.

non-stop _____

non-living _____

non-fiction _____

non-starter _____

non-event _____

non-existent _____

nonsense _____

non-stick _____

nondescript _____

nonconformist _____

Some words can be confused.

in means a position **inside**
into means moving in from **outside**

The mouse is
in the hole.

The mouse ran
into the hole.

between	is used for two of anything	**either**	means one of two people or things
among	is used for more than two	**neither**	means not either of them
who's	means 'who is'	**ever**	means at all times
whose	means 'belonging to whom'	**never**	means at no time

Write the **exact** meanings of these words, using your dictionary to help you.

won ....   bought ....

beat ....   brought ....

teach ....   through ....

learn ....   thorough ....

Rewrite these sentences, choosing the correct word from the brackets.

1   I keep my money (in, into) my purse.

....

2   The children ran (in, into) the school hall.

....

3   (Who's, Whose) that at the door?

....

4   That's the man (who's, whose) car has broken down.

....

5   Nothing (never, ever) happens like that here.

....

6   The dog ran (between, among) the flock of sheep.

....

7   I (brought, bought) some apples from the greengrocer.

....

8   My teacher decided to (learn, teach) us about decimals.

....

Comprehension

Read about **The Norman Conquest**.

After winning the Battle of Hastings in 1066, William of Normandy marched to Westminster and crowned himself King of England. The Conqueror was a strong and ruthless ruler. He was determined to settle and organize the country he had overpowered.

King William sent out teams of officials to make a record of every man, woman and child in his new kingdom. Next he wanted to know how much land there was and what it was used for. Every cow, sheep, chicken and even the fish in the fish ponds had to be counted. The counting was done on people's fingers, in 'hands'. One hand of sheep meant five sheep.

William's officials spoke French and so named the animals in their own French language. They called the pigs 'porc', the cows 'boeuf' and the sheep 'mouton'. To this day we call the meat of these animals pork, beef and mutton.

All the information was written by hand in a great book, called the Domesday Book. The English people called it dooms day, because they now felt that it was their fate or doom to pay taxes to this foreign king.

About the king

Read the question. Put a tick under the correct answer.

1   William conquered England, at the Battle of Hastings, in the year:

    1066   1610   1006   1000
    ☐   ☐   ☐   ☐

2   England's new king came from:

    Bordeaux   Normandy   Ardennes   Marne
    ☐   ☐   ☐   ☐

3   William crowned himself King of England at:

    Hastings   Battle   Canterbury   Westminster
    ☐   ☐   ☐   ☐

4   When he was king, William ruled England with:

    determination   gentleness   weakness   little interest
    ☐   ☐   ☐   ☐

5   William decided that England must be:

    left to look   sold to another   settled and
    after itself   country   organized
    ☐   ☐   ☐

About the Domesday Book

Answer these questions:

1   Who was sent to make the records? ....

2   What did the officials do first? ....

....

3   What **two** things did William   1 ....
    want to know about England?   2 ....

4   Name the living creatures that   1 ....   2 ....
    had to be counted.   3 ....   4 ....

5   How many animals did a man
    possess if he held: a) four hands of sheep? ....

                         b) three hands of cows? ....

6   Write the English word for each of these meats:

            'porc' ....   'boeuf' ....   'mouton' ....

How the information is written

1   Write the word or phrase from the information for:

    having no pity ....   people in authority ....

    conquered ....   having made up your mind ....

2   What is meant by 'paying taxes'? ....

....

3   What does the word Domesday mean? ....

....

4   Explain how the words pork, beef and mutton have become part of the English
    language.

....

....

Handwriting

Using your best joined up handwriting, copy this sentence:

        The Domesday Book is the record of a survey carried out on the
        orders of William I in 1086.

....

....

Grammar

A **conjunction** is a **joining word**.

e.g.   He opened his book **and** began to read.
       He looked for his book, **but** couldn't find it.

Some common **conjunctions** are:

and	or	because	before	when	until	while
but	if	although	after	where	whether	so

Draw a ring round the **conjunctions** in these sentences.

Write the **conjunction** here.

1   I got up and ran downstairs.

2   I heard the alarm, but didn't get up.

3   Linford left school before the bell rang.

4   Sally left the stadium after the last race.

5   Tom laid the table while Kate cooked our supper.

6   Would you like an ice cream or will you have a drink?

7   We went to Trafalgar Square where we saw Nelson's Column.

8   Nancy felt nervous when she saw the big dog.

9   I was angry because it was not my fault.

10   They played the match although it was snowing.

Conjunctions can give **reasons** and explain how or why.

Join these clauses to make sensible sentences. Draw a ring round the conjunctions.

1   I went to bed   until I've finished my homework.

2   You will hurt yourself   although it was raining.

3   I can't watch T.V.   because I felt ill.

4   Yesterday we played tennis   when the mist lifts.

5   We will climb that mountain   if you fall off that ladder.

Write sentences of your own, using the words in capitals as conjunctions.

BUT ....

UNLESS ....

BECAUSE ....

ALTHOUGH ....

IF ....

Using nouns

> Many **adjectives** can be made **from nouns**.
> e.g. The adjective **golden** can be made from the noun **gold**.

Write the adjective formed from each noun:

	Noun	Adjective			Noun	Adjective
1	mist	....		6	giant	....
2	rock	....		7	hero	....
3	friend	....		8	ice	....
4	soap	....		9	pain	....
5	storm	....		10	music	....

> **Nouns** can be formed from **adjectives**.
> e.g. The noun **bone** can be made from the adjective **bony**.

Write the noun formed from each adjective.

	Adjective	Noun			Adjective	Noun
1	sunny	....		6	monstrous	....
2	dusty	....		7	dangerous	....
3	feathery	....		8	poisonous	....
4	foggy	....		9	famous	....
5	sugary	....		10	picturesque	....

> Many **verbs** can be made **from nouns**.
> e.g. The verb **to injure** can be made from the noun **injury**.

Write the verb made from the noun underlined in each sentence: **Verb**

1	The policeman took prompt <u>action</u>.	to act
2	She has a wonderful <u>imagination</u>.	
3	The <u>swimmer</u> reached the drowning boy.	....
4	The prize gave me great <u>satisfaction</u>.	....
5	<u>Assembly</u> lasted nearly an hour.	....

> **Nouns** can be formed from **verbs**.
> e.g. The noun **examination** can be made from the verb **to examine**.

Write the noun formed from the verb in capital letters.

1	to INVITE	I had an .... to the party.
2	to DESCRIBE	He wrote a good .... in his diary.
3	to CHOOSE	There is a .... of books in the library.
4	to ENQUIRE	My teacher made an .... about Rob's absence.
5	to EXPLORE	We made a thorough .... of the area.

Vocabulary

Similes and **metaphors** make word pictures.
Two things which are **compared** with each other, using **as** or **like** are called **similes**.
e.g. We could see people **as small as ants** in the street below.

Complete these **similes**:

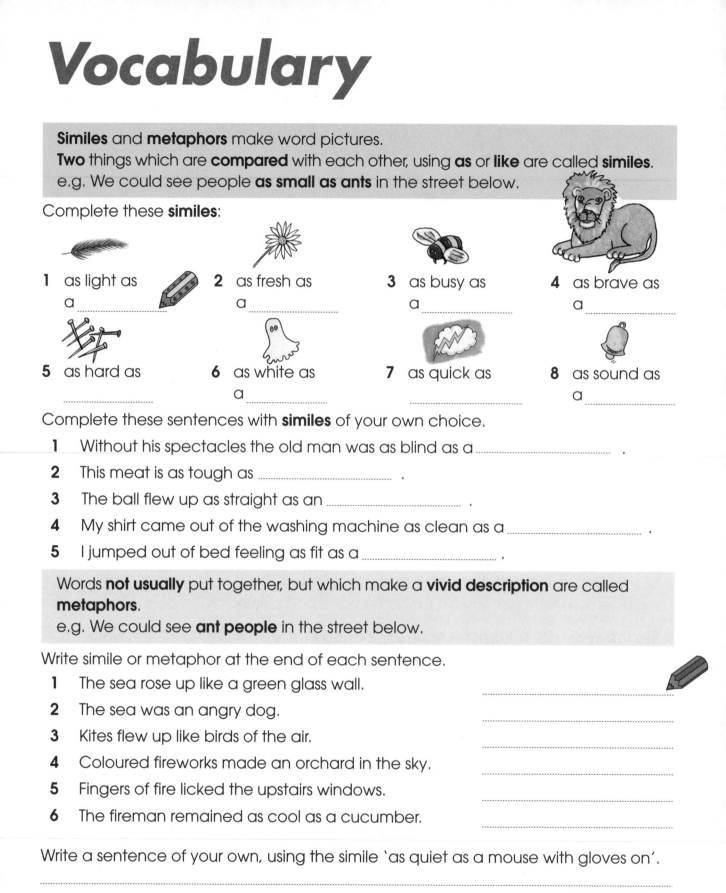

1 as light as
   a _____

2 as fresh as
   a _____

3 as busy as
   a _____

4 as brave as
   a _____

5 as hard as
   _____

6 as white as
   a _____

7 as quick as
   _____

8 as sound as
   a _____

Complete these sentences with **similes** of your own choice.

1   Without his spectacles the old man was as blind as a _____ .

2   This meat is as tough as _____ .

3   The ball flew up as straight as an _____ .

4   My shirt came out of the washing machine as clean as a _____ .

5   I jumped out of bed feeling as fit as a _____ .

Words **not usually** put together, but which make a **vivid description** are called **metaphors**.
e.g. We could see **ant people** in the street below.

Write simile or metaphor at the end of each sentence.

1   The sea rose up like a green glass wall.   _____

2   The sea was an angry dog.   _____

3   Kites flew up like birds of the air.   _____

4   Coloured fireworks made an orchard in the sky.   _____

5   Fingers of fire licked the upstairs windows.   _____

6   The fireman remained as cool as a cucumber.   _____

Write a sentence of your own, using the simile 'as quiet as a mouse with gloves on'.

_____

_____

Write a sentence of your own, using the metaphor 'in the black bandaged night'.

_____

_____

Traditional sayings which express something in an **unusual way** are called **idioms**.

Write one of these **idioms** under the appropriate picture.

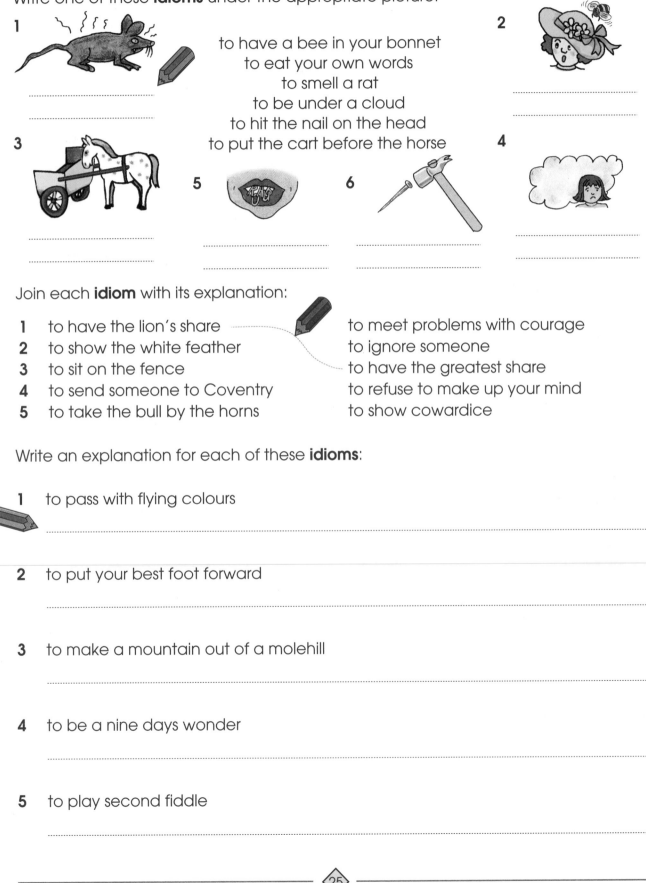

1

to have a bee in your bonnet
to eat your own words
to smell a rat
to be under a cloud
to hit the nail on the head
to put the cart before the horse

2

3

5   6

4

Join each **idiom** with its explanation:

1   to have the lion's share   to meet problems with courage
2   to show the white feather   to ignore someone
3   to sit on the fence   to have the greatest share
4   to send someone to Coventry   to refuse to make up your mind
5   to take the bull by the horns   to show cowardice

Write an explanation for each of these **idioms**:

1   to pass with flying colours

2   to put your best foot forward

3   to make a mountain out of a molehill

4   to be a nine days wonder

5   to play second fiddle

Making notes

Cross out the words **not** important to the meaning.

Write the **key words** in each sentence here.

1   Put the chocolate, milk and brown sugar into a pan.

....

....

2   Heat all the ingredients for 3 minutes.

....

....

3   Pour the sauce, when cool, on ice cream or profiteroles.

....

....

Use these notes to write three complete sentences about making **Sponge Cake.**

1   mix...eggs...flour...
    butter...sugar

1 ....

....

2   mixture...tin...bake...
    30 minutes

2 ....

....

3   decorate...cream...
    strawberries

3 ....

....

Read this recipe for **Lemon Biscuits**. Write **notes** as answers to the questions.

Recipe Card	Questions	Notes
Mix together: 1 egg 100g butter 100g sugar 200g flour	1 What ingredients do you need?	....
grated rind 1 lemon		
Chill mixture until firm. Roll out. Cut into rounds.	2 What must you do before rolling out?	....
	3 What must you do to the baking tin?	....
Bake on a greased tin in a moderate oven for 20 minutes.	4 For how long do you cook the biscuits?	....

Read each sentence.

 Write **key words** for each sentence.

1   Chemistry is a branch of science
    and is the study of chemicals.

2   A chemical reaction is a change
    which takes place when different
    substances are put together.

3   One example of a chemical reaction
    occurs when the ingredients of a
    cake are cooked in an oven.

4   The baking powder reacts with the
    other ingredients of the cake and
    gives off little bubbles.

5   These gas bubbles are carbon
    dioxide which makes the cake rise.

Read this paragraph about another sign of a **Chemical Reation**.

Rust occurs when water and air combine on iron, or on
metals which contain iron. If air and water can be excluded
from iron, it will not rust. Some iron and steel tools are painted
to prevent rusting. However, if the tools become scratched
and the iron is exposed to the air and rain, rusting will take
place.

Write **notes** as answers to these questions: **Notes**

1   What is rust a sign of?

2   What two substances combine to form rust?

3   On what metals can rust form?

4   How can rust be prevented from forming on
    iron and steel tools?

5   What will happen if the paint becomes
    scratched and the metal is exposed again?

Using books

Reference books contain **information**.

Write the title of the book in which you would find **information** about:

1 bars   discords   melody   opera   tempo ....

2 athletics   cricket   hurdling   marathons   squash ....

3 continents   fjords   islands   oceans   rivers ....

4 Agincourt   Balaclava   Bannockburn   Hastings ....

5 abbreviations   nouns   plurals   spelling   verbs ....

6 copper   iron   mercury   radium   zinc ....

> The **contents** of a reference book tell you what you will find in the book.
> The **index** gives details of the main subjects with their page numbers.
> The **glossary** gives the meaning of special words.

Read these special words from the **glossary** of a **geography** text book.
Write the meaning of each one. Use your dictionary to help you.

```
GLOSSARY

altitude... ..............................................................................

climate... ..............................................................................

communications... ..............................................................................

equator... ..............................................................................

fauna... ..............................................................................

flora... ..............................................................................

habitat... ..............................................................................

latitude... ..............................................................................

longitude... ..............................................................................

population... ..............................................................................
```

Reference books contain **facts**.
A **fact** is a true statement which can be **proved**.
e.g. It is raining.

Read these **facts** about **Everyday Inventions**.

The brothers John and William Kellogg invented corn flakes.
In 1849, Walter Hunt, an American, invented the first safety pin.
The telephone was invented by Alexander Graham Bell.
Whitcomb Judson invented the zip fastener in 1893.
In 1853 Elisha Otis invented the first lift.
The brothers Biro invented the first ballpoint pen.

Answer these questions about **facts**:

1   Who invented the first ballpoint pen?

2   In what year was the first lift invented?

3   What did the brothers Kellogg invent?

4   What was the nationality of Walter Hunt?

5   Who invented the telephone?

6   In what year was the zip fastener invented?

An **opinion** is an idea or belief which is **not proved**.
e.g. I have an idea that it will rain today.

In my opinion…
I'd say…

If you ask me…
Surely you think that…

Write **fact** or **opinion** after each of these statements:

1   My hamster is brown with white patches.

2   I think that gerbils are better pets than hamsters.

3   If you ask me, she can't sing in tune.

4   This is the most interesting book ever written.

5   My young sisters are twins.

6   I have a feeling that I shall win the race.

Write this saying in you best joined up handwriting:

'He that agrees against his will,
Is of the same opinion still.'

Test your progress

Write each set of words in alphabetical order.

Welsh	....	conduct	....	chapel	....
Scottish	....	conjure	....	mosque	....
Cornish	....	consent	....	church	....
English	....	continue	....	temple	....
Irish	....	confess	....	monastery	....

Draw lines to link the **antonyms.**

always - - - - - - - - - - happily
slowly   smoothly
unhappily   noisily
quietly   quickly
roughly   never

Write the **prefix** to make a word of opposite meaning.

appear   ....
approve   ....
continue ....
honour   ....
orderly   ....

Draw a ring round the correct **homophone** to complete each sentence.

1   A stallion is a (male, mail) horse.
2   The word (there, their) means belonging to them.
3   (Pray, Prey) is an animal hunted for food by another.
4   To (steel, steal) is to take someone else's property.
5   The collective noun for a group of cows is (herd, heard).

Put the correct **punctuation mark** in each balloon.

1   Susan◯s hat blew off into the road ◯

2   ◯Would you like to come to the park◯◯ asked Leroy◯

3   ◯Hurry up◯◯ called my mother◯

1 | a | | | |
    a book of maps

2 | d | | | | | | | | | |
    a book explaining the
    meaning of words

3 | E | | | | | |
    the language of England

4 | m | | | | | | | | | |
    the science of numbers

5 | h | | | | | | |
    the study of the past

6 | b | a | r | o | | | | |
    measures air pressure

7 | m | i | c | r | o | | | | |
    measures tiny things

8 | z | o | | | | |
    the study of animals

Colour in how many you got right on the ladder and your mistakes on the snake.

Ladder: 50 49 48 47 46 45 44 43 42 41 40 39 38 37 36 35 34 33 32 31 30 29 28 27 26 25 24 23 22 21 20 19 18 17 16 15 14 13 12 11 10 9 8 7 6 5 4 3 2 1

Snake: 1 2 3 4 5 6 7 8 9 10 11 12 13 14 15 16 17 18 19 20 21 22 23 24 25 26 27 28 29 30 31 32 33 34 35 36 37 38 39 40 41 42 43 44 45 46 47 48 49 50

Draw a ring round the **two** verbs which are **synonyms** of the word in capital letters.

1	ANSWER	question	reply	problem	try	respond
2	ASK	task	agree	request	ascend	enquire
3	CATCH	capture	gather	throw	play	trap
4	DIG	number	excavate	hole	burrow	earth
5	FALL	hesitate	plunge	plummet	leaves	quarrel

Write the **adjective** formed from each noun.

1   fog   ....

2   beauty   ....

3   truth   ....

4   curl   ....

5   marvel   ....

Write the **noun** formed from each adjective.

1   sandy   ....

2   smoky   ....

3   gigantic   ....

4   breezy   ....

5   poisonous   ....

Draw a line under the **verb** in each sentence.

1   The dog ran quickly across the road.

2   The goalkeeper fell heavily onto the ball.

3   I replied to the question slowly.

4   She looked at me suspiciously.

5   I am never late for school.

Write the **adverb** here.

....

....

....

....

....

Join these phrases to make sensible sentences.
Draw a ring round the **conjunction**.

1   I shall go to bed

2   You can borrow my ball

3   He looked for his coat

4   Wait at the bus stop

5   Would you like a cake

if you promise to return it.

because I'm so tired.

or a biscuit?

but he couldn't find it.

until I arrive.

Complete these **similes**:

1   as bold as   ....

2   as bright as   ....

3   as mad as   ....

4   as blind as   ....

5   as timid as   ....

6   as .... as snow

7   as .... as an owl

8   as .... as fire

9   as .... as velvet

10   as .... as a feather

Colour in how many you got right on the ladder and your mistakes on the snake.

Answers

1 E H K N   2 P S V Y
3 Y W U S Q   4 A B D E F H I K L M
5 B C D F H I J L

Anderson	Bach
Blume	Beethoven
Dahl	Bizet
Fine	Borodin
Grimm	Brahms
Shakespeare	Byrd

spear	contact	baby
special	contempt	baptize
speed	continue	between
spell	contour	birthday
spend	contract	birthplace

alphabetical order: caravan, cardigan, carnation, carpet, carrot, cart

1 30	2 beetles 36	3 molluscs 39
4 toad 25	5 dogs 16	6 coral 42
7 birds 23	8 rabbit 19	

1 false	2 true	3 true	4 false
5 false	6 true	7 false	8 false

landscape, landowner, landlord/landlady, landslide, landmark

1 Iceland	2 an ancient alphabet
3 a volcano	4 an Icelandic guide
5 for six hundred years	

1 The Professor finds...	2 Axel deciphers an...
3 They decide to...	4 The Professor engages...
5 They set off...	6 They see a...

For example:
1 Professor Lidenbrock is adventurous but a little mad.
2 Axel is much more cautious than his uncle.

1 ancient	document	engage
cautious	mad	silent

For example:
2 The volcano has been dormant for 600 years but it might explode again.
3 The Mistour is a huge column of stones, sand and dust that twists and swirls.

1 future	2 past	3 present	4 past
5 present	6 future		

1 started	2 will come	3 rained
4 is open/opens	5 will arrive	6 swam

past tense	present	future
last week	now	will wear
the year 1066	see	tomorrow
was	is	A.D. 2000
wore	am wearing	will be
jumped		
sang		

	verb	adverb
1	moved	slowly
2	chewed	noisily
3	wandered	away
4	visits	often
5	climbs	clumsily
6	stays	sometimes

biography   geology   microscope
autobiography   archaeology   telescope
paragraph   biology
       sociology
       zoology

1 microscope	2 geology	3 biography
4 zoology	5 telescope	6 biology
7 archaeology	8 autobiography	
9 paragraph	10 sociology	

rough   tough

1 immense, massive
2 perilous, menacing
3 dramatic, sensational
4 void, vacant
5 celebrated, notable
6 diligent, busy

1 commence, being		2 char, scorch
3 pursue, follow		4 detest, dislike
5 launder, purify		6 displease, insult

1 dull	2 talented	3 murky
4 correct	5 simple	6 difficult
7 mild	8 unsightly	9 tranquil
10 destitute		

1 bright radiant	2 companion comrade
3 audience congregation	4 examine inspect
5 observe witness	6 precious valuable
7 discover detect	8 opposite contradictory

1 Henry VIII, born, 1491
2 Henry, reigned, 1509, 1547
3 Cardinal, Wolsey, Lord, Chancellor
4 Wolsey, power, make, rich
5 Hampton Court Palace, built, Wolsey

1 Anne Boleyn...Henry's second wife, mother Elizabeth
2 Elizabeth I...Queen of England, 1558
3 Her reign...45 years, many favourites
4 Raleigh... Elizabeth's favourite, poet, soldier, explorer
5 Tallis...musician, composed, printed, music, Elizabeth's court
6 Shakespeare...Elizabethan writer, 37 plays, poems

1 Drake, Elizabethan sailor
2 Queen, permission, Drake, attack, other countries' ships, take, cargoes
3 Drake, sailed, Spanish ports, America, stole, gold
4 Drake, Spanish, nick-name, 'El Draco', The Dragon

1 Medina Sidonia	2 1588
3 English Channel	4 to invade England
5 Calais harbour	6 violent storm
7 attacked with fire ships	
8 destroyed ships	9 130 10 60

2 you've	3 we're	4 you're	5 she's
6 they're	7 didn't	8 won't	9 couldn't

1 the dog's tail   2 Harry's coat
3 the kangaroo's pouch
4 Mount Everest's summit
5 the Inuit's canoe

the hen's eggs	the bees' wings
the girls' kites	an aeroplane's wings
the monkey's tail	the clowns' noses

1 The sun set over the sea. Hungry seagulls swooped down, over the waves.
2 A full moon cast a beam of light through the trees. There was the missing dog. He was hiding under the thick, leafy bushes.
. , ? " " ' !

1 "Stand!" cried the highwayman, "or I shoot."
2 "Hand over your jewels!" he commanded.
3 "Must you take everything that we have?" quavered the frightened travellers.
4 "I take all," replied Turpin. "Now drive on."

1 bird's	2 cats'	3 ships'
4 girls'	5 donkey's	6 author's

m.p.h.   p.t.o.   R.I.P.   F.A.   E.R.   N.Y.

sent	flower	hole	some
ball	new	right	great
stare	root	profit	sore/saw
piece	serial	style	ring

1 site	2 four	3 main	4 stationary

For example: a lamp or a match
to switch on a lamp   not heavy

1 wrist	2 paw	3 sight	4 touch
5 flowers	6 fish	7 sheep	
8 hospital	9 foot	10 narrow	

1 boy	2 swarm	3 stallion	4 prince
5 finish	6 enemy	7 unpleasant	
8 liquid	9 dry	10 drought	

yell "ow!"